Information for Parents

In literacy lessons teachers will be seeking to encourage their pupils to:

• Read confidently and with understanding;
• Understand phonics and spelling patterns;
• Use neat handwriting with speed and accuracy;
• Expand their vocabulary;
• Appreciate a range of styles in fiction and poetry;
• Understand how stories are structured by the writers' use of settings, characters and plots;
• Read and use non-fiction materials;
• Develop their own writing using techniques of planning, drafting and editing;
• Enjoy reading books;
• Use imagination and inventiveness in their own writing.

Throughout the primary years the children will address their literacy work at three levels: word level, sentence level and text level.

Word level work includes word recognition, phonics, spelling, vocabulary and handwriting.

Sentence level work covers grammatical awareness, sentence construction and punctuation.

Text level work covers comprehension of reading and the composition of writing. It includes working with fiction, non-fiction and poetry.

Many schools operate a 'literacy hour' where they address all the aspects of literacy directly, but they will also seek to cover some aspects through other subjects throughout the school day.

In the **Literacy Now** series we provide practice materials for word level, sentence level and text level work, matched appropriately to children's ages. The books are designed to be used by parents working with their children to provide extra practice, whether out of a need to improve particular aspects of the children's progress or simply for the fun of working on English at home.

Literacy Now
for ages 6–7

Excellent practice for literacy

Your child will enjoy working through this book alongside you. Most children will need help reading the short passages of writing and answering the questions. You may like to read the passages to your child. This will help her/him to gain confidence.

The experience of reading and writing with one-to-one support will be of enormous value to your child and will help to build solid foundations for her/his education.

Andrew Brodie

Animal facts

Here is some interesting information about two Australian animals.

The Koala

The koala is often called a koala bear because it looks like a bear, but it is not really a bear at all.

The koala is mainly coloured grey with a white front. It has large ears, a large nose and very sharp teeth.

A baby koala is known as a cub and lives for the first few months of its life in its mother's pouch. When it is a little older it clings to its mother's back as she travels from tree to tree.

A koala lives, eats and sleeps in eucalyptus trees. Most of the day is spent sleeping. When the koala is awake it is busy eating eucalyptus leaves.

The Kangaroo

The red kangaroo moves very quickly by taking large leaps. Each leap can be as long as 10 metres.

The kangaroo can stand very tall on its strong back legs. It has small front legs that are used like arms.

It is usually a reddish colour, but it can be grey, and has a small head with large ears.

The baby kangaroo is called a Joey and lives in a pouch on the front of its mother. The Joey lives there for about eight months. Kangaroos feed mainly on grass.

Animal facts

How much do you know?

Fill in the gaps in the sentences below.

Koalas eat _ _ _ _ _ _ _ _ _ _ leaves and kangaroos eat _ _ _ _ _.

The koala spends most of the day _ _ _ _ _ _ _ _ _ .

A kangaroo can travel as far as ten _ _ _ _ _ _ _ with each leap.

A baby koala is called a _ _ _ and a baby kangaroo is called a _ _ _ _.

Koalas and kangaroos live in _ _ _ _ _ _ _ _ _ _.

Spelling 'oa' words

Read and copy these words.

koala   foal   road   float   cloak

_____ _____ _____ _____ _____

_____ _____ _____ _____ _____

_____ _____ _____ _____ _____

Kit and Roo

Kit Koala was clinging to a branch in his usual dozy way. He had just had a huge meal of eucalyptus leaves (his favourite food) and was looking forward to a nice long nap.

Suddenly Rob Roo bounced right into the tree Kit was on.

"Oh my goodness," said Kit, "Is it an earthquake?"

"Sorry," squeaked Rob, "I bounced too high and hit your tree."

Kit liked to talk to Rob when he wasn't eating or sleeping, so he slowly climbed down from his branch to find out where his friend was going in such a rush.

Now answer these questions.

1 What sort of animal was Kit?

_____

2 Name Kit's favourite food.

_____

Kit and Roo

3 Name three things Kit liked to do.

_____

4 How did Rob Roo move?

_____

5 What did Kit think had happened when Rob bounced into the tree?

_____

Synonyms

Choose a word from the box that means the same (or nearly the same) as each of the words below.

> jump   normal   fast
> best   hurry   chat
> holding   sleepy   mostly

bounce _____

dozy _____

usual _____

clinging _____

mainly _____

favourite _____

rush _____

talk _____

quick _____

Days and months

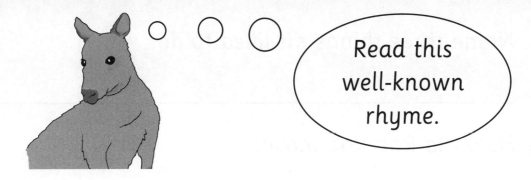

Read this well-known rhyme.

Monday's child is fair of face,
Tuesday's child is full of grace.
Wednesday's child is full of woe,
Thursday's child has far to go.
Friday's child is loving and giving,
Saturday's child works hard for a living.
And the child that is born on the seventh day
Is bonny and blithe, and good and gay.

Write the missing letters for each day.
Match the type of person to the day of the week.
The first two have been done for you.

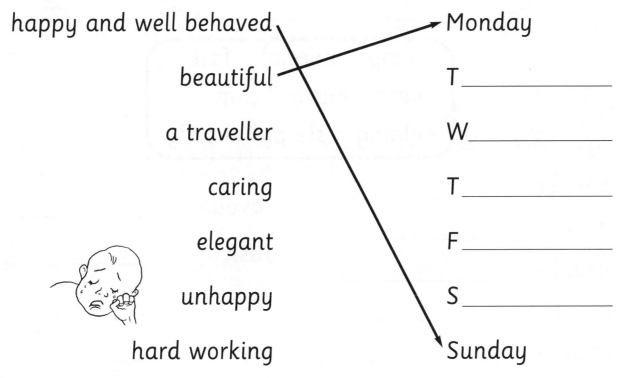

happy and well behaved → Monday

beautiful

a traveller   W_____

caring   T_____

elegant   F_____

unhappy   S_____

hard working → Sunday

T_____

Days and months

Thirty days has September,
April, June and November.
All the rest have thirty-one,
Excepting February alone,
And that has twenty-eight days clear
And twenty-nine in each leap year.

Answer these questions.

1 Which month usually has twenty-eight days?

_____

2 Which months have thirty days?

_____   _____

_____   _____

3 Look at the list of months below.

January   February   March   April   May   June   July

August   September   October   November   December

Write the names of the months that have thirty-one days.

_____   _____   _____

_____   _____   _____

_____

Adjectives

Adjectives are describing words.

They help make our reading and writing more interesting.

Use adjectives from the box to complete the passage below. Use each word only once!

bedtime	flickering	high	cosy
warm	deep	distant	soft
friendly	cheerful		

Long ago in a _____ land full of _____ mountains lived a family of _____ trolls. They made _____ homes inside _____ caves in the mountainside. Each evening the trolls would light a _____ fire and sit around it telling _____ stories. They liked to watch the _____ flames die down before climbing into their beds and falling asleep. Every morning they went outside, stood on the _____ green grass and sang _____ songs before breakfast to greet the new day.

Adjectives

Answer these questions.

1 Who lived in a land full of high mountains?

_____

_____

2 How did they keep warm in the evening?

_____

_____

3 What did the trolls do while sitting around the fire?

_____

_____

4 What did they do before breakfast?

_____

_____

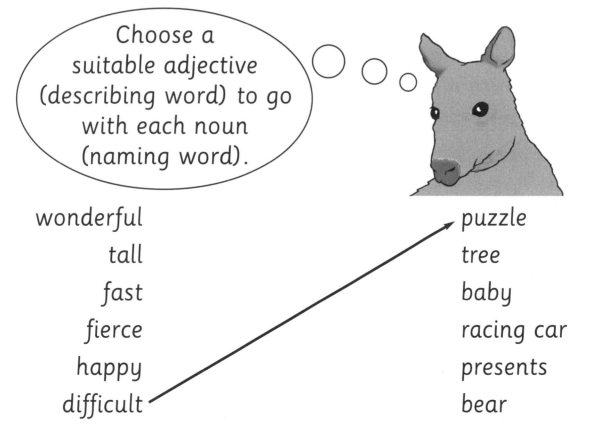

Choose a suitable adjective (describing word) to go with each noun (naming word).

wonderful
tall
fast
fierce
happy
difficult

puzzle
tree
baby
racing car
presents
bear

Compound words

Jake was on holiday with his family. They were staying in a very unusual holiday home: it was a windmill. The windmill stood on a hillside and was surrounded by bluebells.

Each floor had a round carpet and even the cupboards had rounded backs so they fitted snugly against the walls.

The stairs went up the curved walls, and at the very top was Jake's bedroom. It was small, round and cosy and had spectacular views across the countryside.

Compound words

Answer these questions.

1 Which wild flowers grew around the windmill?

_____

2 What was at the top of the windmill?

_____

3 Why were the carpets round?

_____

Teaspoon, necklace and **railway** are compound words.

A compound word is a word made of two or more smaller words.

Read the text again.
You should be able to find six compound words.
Write them on the lines below.

_____   _____

_____   _____

_____   _____

Wesley's pet

Wesley wanted a pet. His friends all had pets. Mike had a cat called Pebbles, Jen had a dog called Boots, Imran had two gerbils called Porridge and Cornflake, and Millie had a rabbit called Misty. Wesley's parents had never allowed him to have a pet to look after.

Now answer these questions. ◯ ◯

Ring the correct answers.

1 What did Wesley want?

a dog   a pet   a hamster   some fish

2 What was the name of the rabbit?

Mike   Millie   Wesley   Misty

3 Who had a dog called Boots?

Jen   Jan   Imran   Millie

4 What sort of animal was the pet named Pebbles?

dog   gerbil   rabbit   cat

5 What sort of animal was the pet named Porridge?

dog   gerbil   rabbit   cat

Wesley's pet

One day Wesley's parents said, "Come into the lounge, we have a surprise for you."

Wesley ran into the lounge. There was a box there. He looked into the box. Two little eyes were in a small, black furry head. It was a new kitten. The kitten mewed. Wesley carefully lifted the kitten up. The kitten purred happily. Wesley was very excited. He had a pet to care for. He couldn't wait to tell his friends.

Now answer these questions. You will need to write the answers on the lines.

1 In which room did Wesley find the surprise?

_____

2 What was the surprise?

_____

3 What was the kitten in?

_____

4 What did Wesley do to the kitten?

_____

5 How did Wesley feel?

_____

Abigail gets lost

"Hold my hand, Abigail," said Mum, "so that you don't get lost." Abigail and Mum were in a big and very busy shop.

Abigail held Mum's hand quite tightly for a while. Then, while Mum was busy looking at clothes, Abigail saw a sign with the word TOYS on it in very large capital letters.

Without thinking, Abigail let go of Mum's hand and went to look at the toys. She looked at dolls' houses, garden swings, games, puzzles and lots of other things.

She looked around to tell Mum what she had seen, but Mum was not there. Abigail was suddenly very frightened. She was lost!

Ring the correct answers to the questions.

1 Where were Mum and Abigail?

at the market   in a shop   in a playground

2 Why did Mum want Abigail to hold her hand?

so she wasn't naughty

so she wouldn't look at the toys

so she looked at the clothes

so she couldn't get lost

Abigail gets lost

Abigail began to cry.

A lady working in the toy department asked her what was wrong.

"I have lost my mum," sobbed Abigail. The lady had a special microphone. She spoke into it. Her voice could be heard very loudly in all of the shop.

She said, "If anyone has lost a little girl, please go to the toy department where she is waiting for her mother."
Very soon Abigail could see Mum rushing towards her.

Mum hugged Abigail and Abigail hugged Mum. Abigail held Mum's hand very tightly as they finished the shopping.

Answer these questions.

1 Who helped Abigail?

    a policeman   a lady working in the shop

    a lady doing her shopping   Abigail's mum

2 Why did Abigail hold Mum's hand tightly as they finished the shopping?

_____

_____

The alphabet

This rhyme has been used for many years to help children learn the alphabet.

A   B   C   D   E   F   G
Little Robin Redbreast sitting on a tree.

H   I   J   K   L   M   N
He fell in love with little Jenny Wren.

O   P   Q   R   S   T   U
Dear little Jenny, I want to marry you.

V   W   X   Y   Z
Poor little Jenny she blushed quite red.

Now answer these questions.

1　Which words in the poem rhyme with the following letters?

G _____   U _____

Z _____   N _____

2　What was the name of the wren?

_____

Circle the correct answer.

3　What did the robin want to do?

fly away   blush red   marry the wren

16

The alphabet

4 Try writing the alphabet in the correct order. Look at the poem <u>afterwards</u> to see if you got it right. Use capital letters.

A _____

_____

_____

5 Did you get it right?
Now try again using lower case letters.

a _____

_____

_____

Sort the words below into alphabetical order. They are all words taken from the poem.

robin	wren	blushed
little	tree	sitting
quite	poor	fell you

1 _____   6 _____

2 _____   7 _____

3 _____   8 _____

4 _____   9 _____

5 _____   10 _____

The journey

The first word of each sentence must begin with a capital letter.

Names of people and places must also begin with a capital letter.

The story below has no capital letters.
Write the story again and put capital letters in the correct places. Use your best handwriting.

mum, dad and faith were going to london for a week's holiday. it was a long way to go in the car and faith thought she would be very bored on the journey.

_____

_____

_____

_____

_____

on the way faith saw the sign to stansted airport and she thought how exciting it would be flying to some distant country.

_____

_____

_____

_____

18

The journey

while she was daydreaming faith suddenly heard dad saying, "nearly there now," and they were soon parking the car outside their hotel.

_____

_____

_____

_____

_____

faith was looking forward so much to all the things they had planned to do in london.

_____

_____

_____

_____

_____

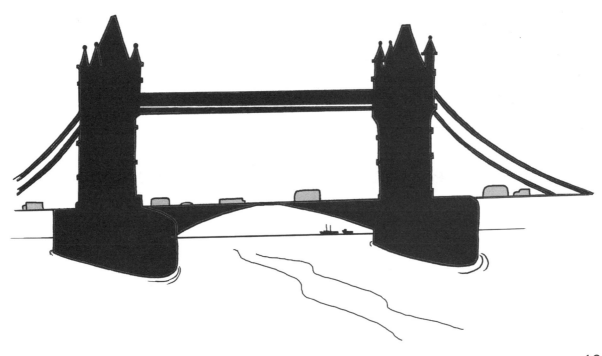

✓ 8 . V . 08

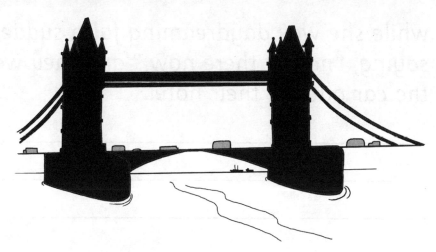

The questions on this page are all about the story on pages 18 and 19.

1 Who was going to London?

_____

2 Why were they going to London?

_____

3 Name the airport they passed. _____

4 What did Faith daydream about?

_____

_____

5 Where did Dad park the car?

_____

_____

6 Write five words that were not at the beginning of a sentence but did need to start with a capital letter

_____ _____

_____ _____

Proper nouns

In the box below are names of towns and cities. There are also some names of people. Write the names in the correct lists.

Cardiff   Norwich   Ricky   London
Glasgow   Jon   Craig   York
Manchester   Jasdeep   Exeter
Abigail   Ben   Maggie

Beijing

Places	People
_____	_____
_____	_____
_____	_____
_____	_____
_____	_____
_____	_____
_____	_____

Now arrange each list of names in alphabetical order.

Places	People
_____	_____
_____	_____
_____	_____
_____	_____
_____	_____
_____	_____

Fish

There are many different kinds of fish. Fish live in water, breathe through gills and use their fins to move about.

Most fish have scales covering their bodies, and all fish have bones (a skeleton) inside them.

Colourful fish

Some fish are very colourful. They use their colours to help them survive. Sometimes spots or stripes provide camouflage.

Flat fish

Fish that live on the sea bed are often flat, so that they can lie unseen on the bottom of the sea.

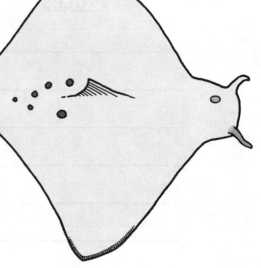

Circle the correct answers.

1 How would you describe this text?

poetry   information   fiction   song

2 Fish breathe through ...

lungs   mouths   fins   gills

3 Fish live in ...

water   wafer   waiter   walker

22

Fish

Write the answers to these questions.

1 Where are flat fish often found?

_____

2 Why do some fish have spots or stripes?

_____

3 Write the two sub-headings that can be found in the text.

_____   _____

4 What covers the bodies of most fish? _____

5 For what do fish use their fins? _____

_____

Present and past tense

Information texts are usually written in the present tense:

Some fish <u>are</u> very colourful.

Stories are usually written in the past tense:

The fish <u>were</u> very colourful.

A terrible tiger tale

One sunny day, Tim went with his parents to visit the zoo. Whilst his mother and father were watching the penguins being fed, Tim got bored and wandered away.

Tim was a naughty boy. He saw the sign saying TIGERS. Tim went to see the tigers.

When no-one was looking, Tim climbed over the fence to get closer to the tigers. This was a very silly thing to do. He stood very close to a large tiger. It was amazing. Such strong legs, such bold stripes, such a powerful head and such an enormous mouth!

The mouth opened. Tim gasped at the sight of the massive pointed teeth.

"What fun this is!" Tim said to himself. "Nobody else would be brave enough to get this close to such a huge animal."

That night the Tiger didn't eat any tea – he was already rather full!

Answer these questions.

1 Who went to visit the zoo?

_____

2 What was the weather like that day?

_____

24

A terrible tiger tale

3 Write three words found in the story, that help you to know how big the tiger is.

_____ _____ _____

4 What happened to Tim at the end of the story? Explain why you think this.

_____

_____

_____

_____

Read these words.
They all end with the same sound.

where	wear	air	chair
scare	bear	bare	stair
pair	pear	care	mare
rare	hair	fair	hare

Choose the correct word to go with each picture.

  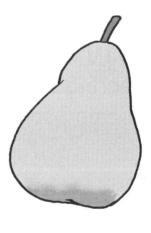

_____ _____

_____

Would you?

Would you like to fly a kite,
Learn to juggle while riding a bike,
Travel the world on a supersonic jet,
Feed the world's most enormous pet,
Lay down and sleep on a bed of nails,
Weigh an elephant on kitchen scales,
Count all the animals in a zoo?
I'd like to do these things – would you?

Would you enjoy a ride on a horse,
A plate of chips with tomato sauce,
Climbing the tallest tree in the world,
Growing your hair long and having it curled,
Swimming in a shark-infested sea,
(You'd have to do that one without me!)
Wearing smart clothes that are fresh and new?
I'd enjoy some of those things – would you?

Would you?

Now answer these questions. Circle the correct answers.

1 What sort of writing have you just read?

fiction   non-fiction   poem   description

2 What word is used to rhyme with **nails**?

rails   scales   tales   pails

3 What word is used to rhyme with **curled**?

swirled   world   curled   twirled

4 Which of the activities would the poet not have enjoyed doing?

_____

5 Read the poem again and choose which of the activities you would not like to do. Write it below.

_____

ou and **ow** can sometimes sound the same in a word.
Read and copy these words.

crown   found   house   clown

_____ _____ _____ _____

round   crowd   cloud   shout

_____ _____ _____ _____

Opposites

The three children were sitting in the garden.
"What shall we do?" asked Luke.
"Lets play opposites," suggested Mel.
"What's that?" asked the others, looking puzzled.
"It's easy," explained Mel, "one person is the leader and the others are followers. The leader gives an instruction and the followers do the opposite. I'll be the leader first," she added.

"Stand up!" she commanded. The others sat down.
The next instruction was "sit down" so they stood up.
Then "turn to the left," so they turned to the right.
"My turn to be the leader now," said Scott. "Walk quickly!" They all walked slowly.
"Look happy!" so they all looked sad.
Before they knew it, it was tea time. They had all enjoyed the game.

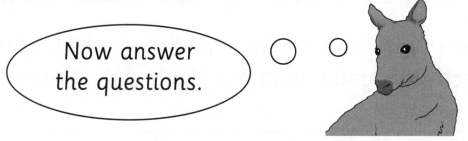

Now answer the questions.

1 How many children were in the story? _____

2 Write their names _____ _____ _____

3 Why was the game called **opposites**?

_____

_____

Opposites

4 Write five pairs of words that are opposites and can be found in the story.

_____ _____

_____ _____   _____ _____

_____ _____   _____ _____

Write the word that is the opposite of each of the following words. Use the words from the Word Bank.

heavy   _____

light   _____

strong   _____

long   _____

before   _____

in   _____

loud   _____

many   _____

forward   _____

hot   _____

kind   _____

WORD BANK
short
unkind
dark
light
backward
after
cold
out
soft
few
weak

The piano

Read these interesting facts about the piano.

♫ The first piano was made around three hundred years ago.

♫ The piano is a **keyboard** instrument.

♫ The keyboard has black notes and white notes. These are called **keys** and they are pressed down to make sounds.

♫ The harder the keys are pressed the louder the sound is.

♫ The original name of this instrument was **pianoforte**, meaning **soft-loud** in Italian.

♫ There are two main types of piano – the **upright** piano and the **grand** piano.

♫ A person who plays the piano is called a **pianist**.

The piano

Answer these questions.

1 The full name for the piano is the pianoforte – what does pianoforte mean?

_____

2 In what language is the word pianoforte?

_____

3 Name the two main types of piano.

_____

4 What sort of instrument is the piano?

_____

5 What two colours are the piano keys?

_____

6 How can a pianist make the notes sound louder?

_____

Nouns and verbs

Nouns are **naming** words.

Verbs are **doing** words.

Here are some nouns:

tin   **lamp**

desk   **bucket**

These are all
names of things.

Here are some verbs:

laugh   **go**

sing   **write**

These are all
actions we can do.

Read these words, then decide which ones are nouns and which ones are verbs. Write them in the correct boxes.

table   chuckle   walk   girl   play   pen

book   laugh   run   sister   boy   piano

Nouns	**Verbs**